Italian to learn before
(or whilst on holiday)

CW00921052

Challenges to speak Italian on holiday
How many of the challenges can you complete?

Are you going to Italy soon?

In Italy, the people speak Italian and I find it fun speaking Italian whenever I go to Italy. Why don't you try and learn some Italian words and phrases before you go?

In the first section of this book there are lots of fun activities to do to help you learn some Italian. And then when you are in Italy, see how many of the 15 challenges from the second part of this book that you can complete.

To say hello in Italian we say Ciao.

To say my name is we say mi chiamo then whatever your name is.

Answer Antonio by writing **Ciao** (hello) and **mi chiamo** (then your name).

Ciao,   mi   chiamo

_____ , ____ _____ _____ .

Essential Italian words

Ciao
(Hi or Bye)

Buon giorno
(Good day)

per favore
(please)

grazie
(thank you)

Buon pomeriggio
(Good afternoon)

sì
(yes)

no
(no)

Buona sera
(Good evening)

Buona notte
(Good night)

Arrivederci
(Good bye)

How do you say the following in Italian?:

(Look at page 2 for the Italian words.)

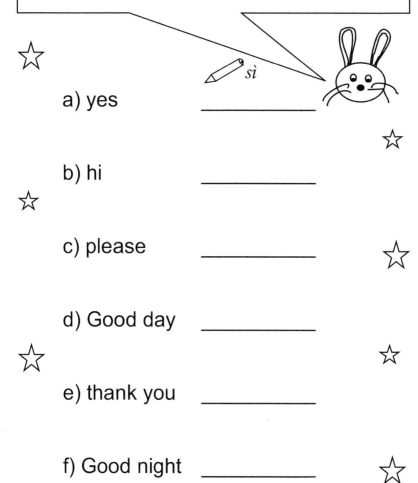

sì

a) yes _____

b) hi _____

c) please _____

d) Good day _____

e) thank you _____

f) Good night _____

g) Good bye _____

3

What Italian word is it?

Rearrange the letters in each bag to find an Italian word:

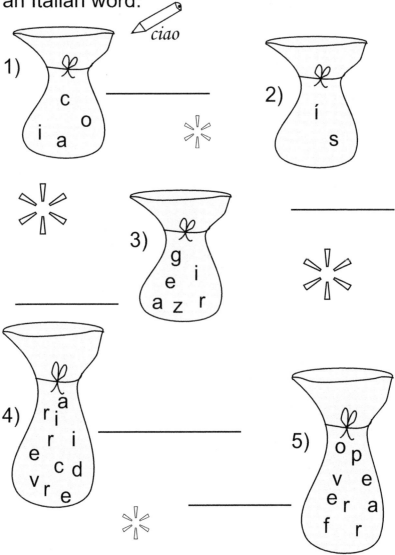

ciao

1) c o i a _____

2) í s _____

3) g i e a z r _____

4) a r i r i e c d v r e _____

5) o p v e e r a f r _____

(The 5 words that are hidden above all appear on page 2)

Come stai? (How are you?)

Come stai?	How are you?
Bene	Good
Così così	So so
Male	Not good

1) How are the children feeling?
Complete the missing letters in the speech bubbles (The words above will help you):

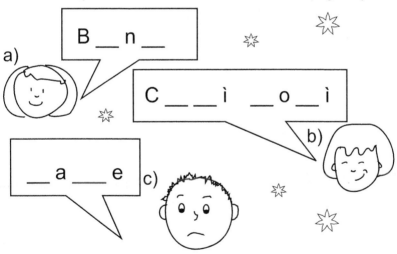

a) B _ n _

b) C _ _ ì _ o _ ì

c) _ a _ _ e

2) Come stai?

(Write in Italian how you are feeling today) _____

5

Copy the Italian words for the numbers:

1   uno

uno

_____

2   due

_____

3   tre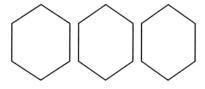

_____

4   quattro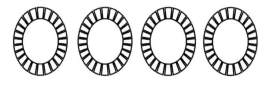

_____

5   cinque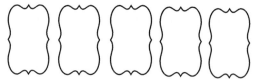

_____

6   sei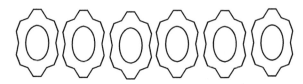

_____

7 sette

_____

8 otto

_____

9 nove

_____

10 dieci

_____

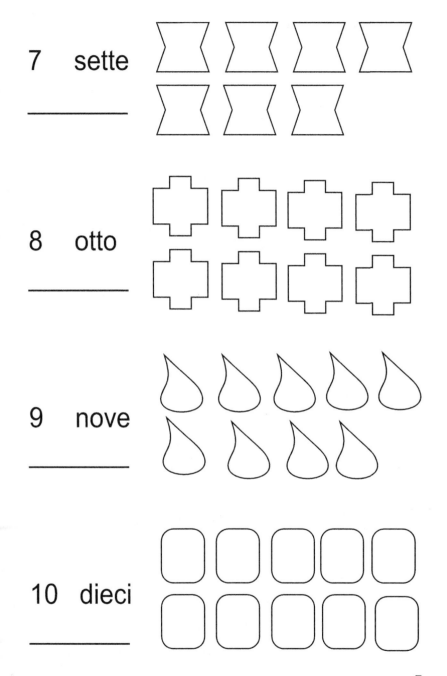

How do you say these numbers in Italian?

a) _due_ _____

b) _____

c) _____

d) _____

e) _____

f) _____

1	**2**	**3**	**4**	**5**	**6**
uno	due	tre	quattro	cinque	sei

8

Asking for things

Ask for the following number of things by saying the number of items followed by **per favore** (please):

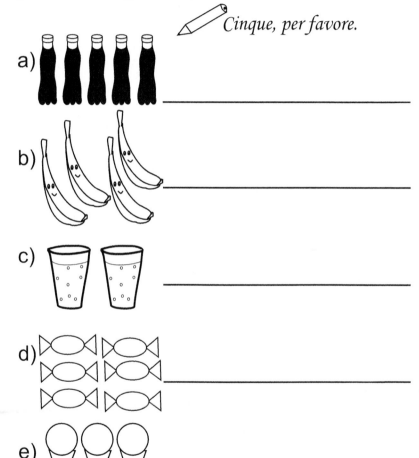

Cinque, per favore.

a) _____

b) _____

c) _____

d) _____

e) _____

1	2	3	4	5	6
uno	due	tre	quattro	cinque	sei

Match the Italian words to the correct number:

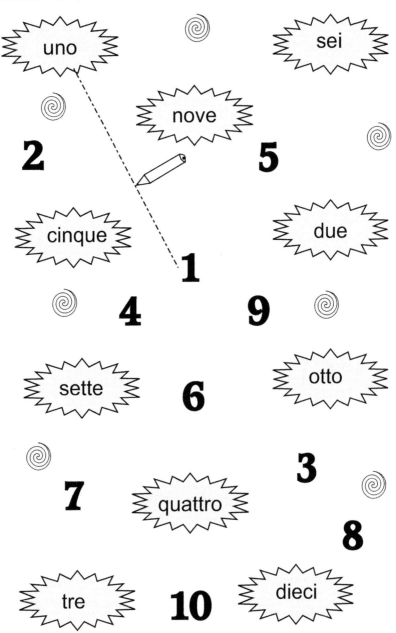

How many of the numbers below can you find?:
(One number is missing.)

UNO   DUE   TRE   QUATTRO   CINQUE

SEI   SETTE   OTTO   NOVE   DIECI

Which number between 1 and 10 is missing?

_____

Bevande (drinks)

Copy the Italian words:

 un'acqua minerale
un'acqua minerale

_____

  una Coca–Cola

_____

 un succo d'arancia

_____

  una limonata

_____

 un tè

un caffè

_____

_____

What drink is it?

Look through the centre of the shapes.
Write the Italian word for the drink you see:

1) *un succo d'arancia*

2)

_____   _____

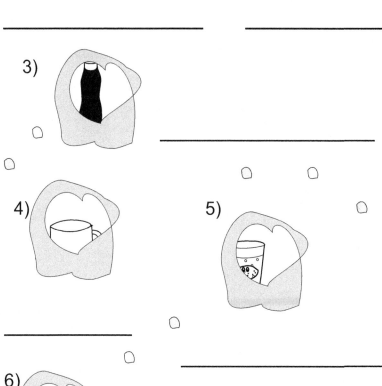

3)

_____

4)

5)

_____

_____

6)

_____

Lets order some drinks!

Vorrei = I would like   per favore = please

Complete the following sentences:

un ' acqua   minerale

 1) Vorrei ____ _____ _____,
per favore.

 2) Vorrei ____ _____ _____,
per favore.

 3) Vorrei ___ _____,
per favore.

 4) _____ _____ _____ ,
per favore.

 5) _____ ____ _____ ,

_____ _____.

6) _____ _____ _____ ,

_____ _____.

| una limonata | un'acqua minerale | un tè |
| una Coca-Cola | un succo d'arancia | un caffè |

■ Asking if they have certain drinks ■

> Avete …….?   Do you have…..?

Imagine a coffee shop is running out of drinks! These are the only drinks available:

Some customers are asking if you have certain drinks.
If the drink is shown above answer sì (yes).
If the drink is not shown answer no. *no*

1) Avete una Coca-Cola light? _____
   (Do you have a diet coke?)

2) Avete una limonata?   _____

3) Avete un succo d'arancia?   _____

4) Avete un caffè?   _____

5) Avete una Coca-Cola?   _____

6) Avete un'acqua minerale?   _____

La colazione (breakfast)

il pane
(bread)

il cornetto
(croissant)

il burro
(butter)

la marmellata
(jam)

i pomodori
(tomatoes)

il prosciutto
(ham)

il formaggio
(cheese)

16

Draw the following:

il cornetto

il pane

i pomodori

il formaggio

la marmellata

il burro

17

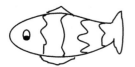

Eating out

pesce
(fish)

hamburger
(hamburger)

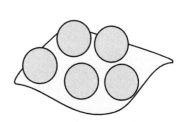

pollo fritto
(fried chicken)

polpette
(meatballs)

patatine
(chips)

riso
(rice)

insalata
(salad)

18

Match the Italian words to the pictures:

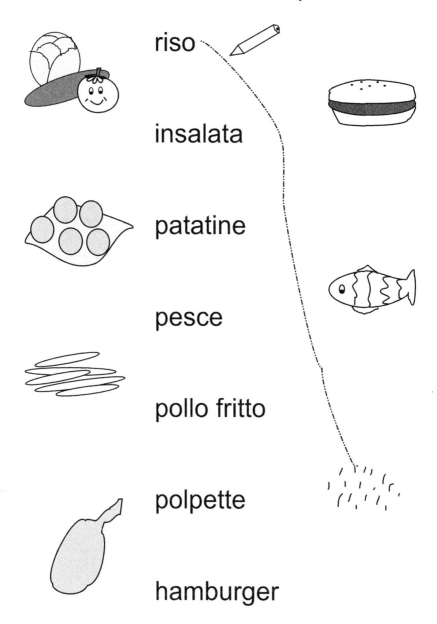

riso

insalata

patatine

pesce

pollo fritto

polpette

hamburger

MENU

Pollo con insalata	€ 8
Pesce con patatine	€ 7
Polpette con riso	€ 9
Hamburger con patatine	€ 6
Hamburger con formaggio	€ 4

●○●○●○●○●○●○ ●○●○●○●○●○●○

In Italy, the people use euros to pay for things. The euro sign looks like this: €
How much does the following cost?

9 euros

1) meatballs with rice _____

2) hamburger with chips _____

3) chicken with salad _____

4) fish with chips _____

5) hamburger with cheese _____

Word search

Find the following words:

PROSCIUTTO
FORMAGGIO
POMODORI
INSALATA
PATATINE
PANE
PESCE
BURRO
POLLO
RISO

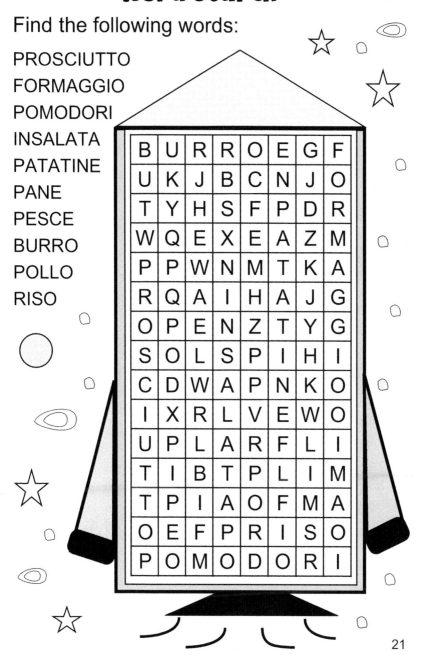

B	U	R	R	O	E	G	F
U	K	J	B	C	N	J	O
T	Y	H	S	F	P	D	R
W	Q	E	X	E	A	Z	M
P	P	W	N	M	T	K	A
R	Q	A	I	H	A	J	G
O	P	E	N	Z	T	Y	G
S	O	L	S	P	I	H	I
C	D	W	A	P	N	K	O
I	X	R	L	V	E	W	O
U	P	L	A	R	F	L	I
T	I	B	T	P	L	I	M
T	P	I	A	O	F	M	A
O	E	F	P	R	I	S	O
P	O	M	O	D	O	R	I

La pasta

Italy is famous for it's lovely pasta dishes.
Here are a few common sauces:

alla napoletana
(tomato sauce)

alla bolognese
(meat sauce)

alla carbonara
(bacon in a creamy sauce)

alla panna
(with cream)

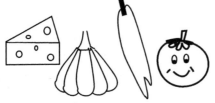

all'arrabbiata
(a spicy tomato sauce made with garlic, tomatoes,
red chili peppers and cheese)

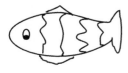

al pesto
(basil, oil and garlic sauce)

al salmone
(with salmon)

There are lots of different pasta shapes:
Copy the Italian words and the pictures:

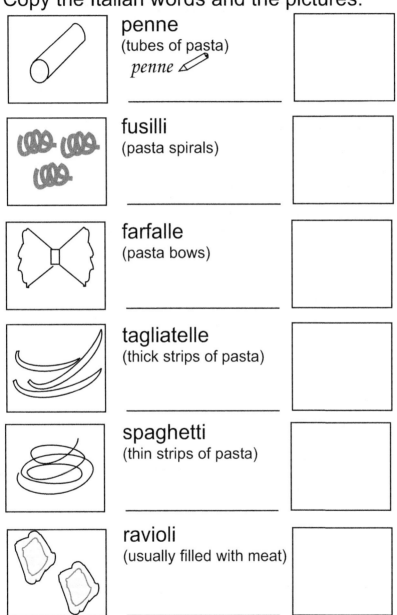

penne
(tubes of pasta)
penne

fusilli
(pasta spirals)

farfalle
(pasta bows)

tagliatelle
(thick strips of pasta)

spaghetti
(thin strips of pasta)

ravioli
(usually filled with meat)

Cosa desiderano? (What do they want?)

Anna: Spaghetti alla carbonara

Marco: Ravioli all'arrabbiata

Elena: Tagliatelle al salmone

Antonio: Penne alla napoletana

Susanna: Farfalle al pesto

Write the name of the person who orders:

1) filled pasta shapes in a spicy   *Marco*
   tomato sauce
   _____

2) tubes of pasta in tomato sauce _____

3) thick strips of pasta with salmon _____

4) Bow pasta shapes in a basil,
   olive oil and garlic sauce.
   _____

5) thin strips of pasta in a creamy
   bacon sauce
   _____

Can you help the waiter?

Fill in the missing letters in order to reveal the waiter's food order:

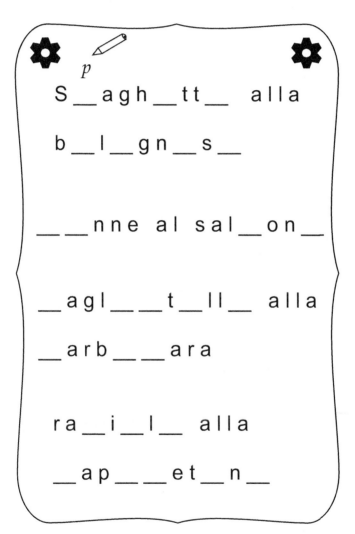

p

S __ a g h __ t t __   a l l a

b __ l __ g n __ s __

__ __ n n e   a l   s a l __ o n __

__ a g l __ __ t __ l l __   a l l a

__ a r b __ __ a r a

r a __ i __ l __   a l l a

__ a p __ __ e t __ n __

 See pages 22 - 24 for the types of pasta
and the pasta sauces.

Pizza toppings

Copy the Italian words::

funghi

funghi

_____

cipolle

_____

salame

_____

formaggio

_____

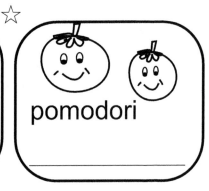

pomodori

_____

prosciutto

_____

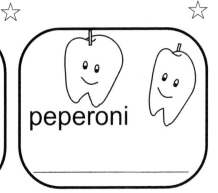

peperoni

_____

Match the Italian words to the pictures:

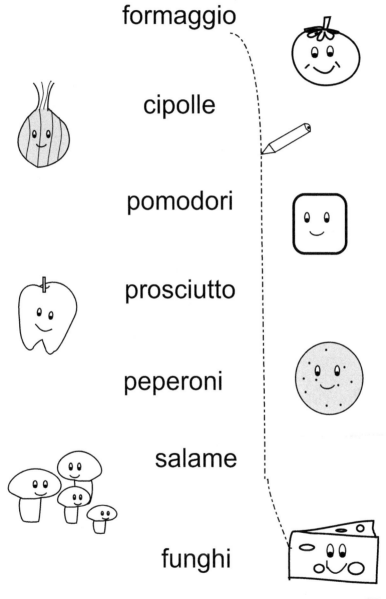

formaggio

cipolle

pomodori

prosciutto

peperoni

salame

funghi

■ Help the chef prepare the pizzas! ■

Draw the correct ingredients on the pizzas:

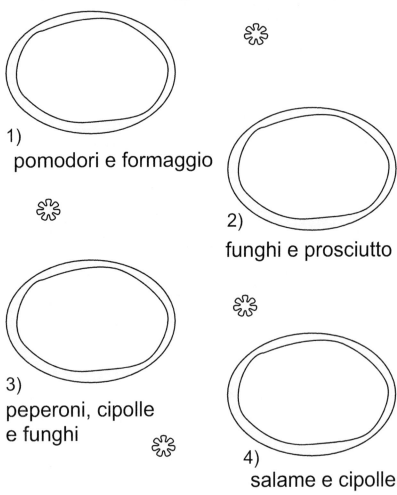

1)
pomodori e formaggio

2)
funghi e prosciutto

3)
peperoni, cipolle
e funghi

4)
salame e cipolle

	pomodori = tomatoes	formaggio = cheese
❄	prosciutto = ham	peperoni = peppers ❄
	cipolle = onions	salame = salami
	funghi = mushrooms	

Vorrei una pizza, per favore

(I would like a pizza, please)

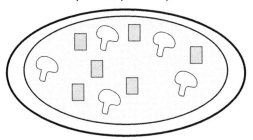

Help a lady remember her family's pizza order by filling in the missing letters:

una pi __ __ a con __ u __ ghi

e c __ p __ lle

una __ __ zza con __ al __ __ e

e pr __ __ ciu __ __ o

una pizza con __ om __ dori,

__ orm __ __ __ io e p __ p __ roni

una __ izz __ con fu __ __ hi

29

Word challenge

Arrange the Italian words below on the page opposite according to it's food type:

funghi

tagliatelle

salame

insalata

patatine

cipolle

pomodori

spaghetti

pesce

pollo fritto

farfalle

ravioli

prosciutto

fusilli

peperoni

salmone

polpette

hamburger

penne

Italian words for meat, chicken or fish

pollo fritto

Italian words for vegetables or salad

Italian words for types of pasta

Ice cream flavours

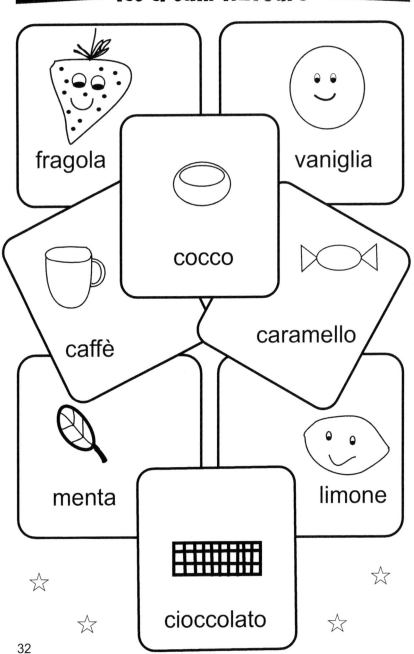

fragola

vaniglia

cocco

caffè

caramello

menta

limone

cioccolato

32

Match the Italian and English words:

coconut  cocco

chocolate

fragola

mint

cioccolato

menta

strawberry

lemon   limone

coffee

caramel

vanilla   caffè

vaniglia

caramello

33

Asking for an ice cream

After **un gelato** you need either **al** or **alla** before the ice cream flavour.

Underline the words **al** in blue, and the **alla** in red:

un gelato alla vaniglia

un gelato al limone

un gelato alla fragola

un gelato al cocco

un gelato al caffè

un gelato alla menta

un gelato al cioccolato

un gelato al caramello

Which ice creams need **al** before the flavour?

lemon

_____ _____ _____ _____ _____

Which ones need **alla** before the flavour?

_____ _____ _____

Draw the correct number of ice creams:

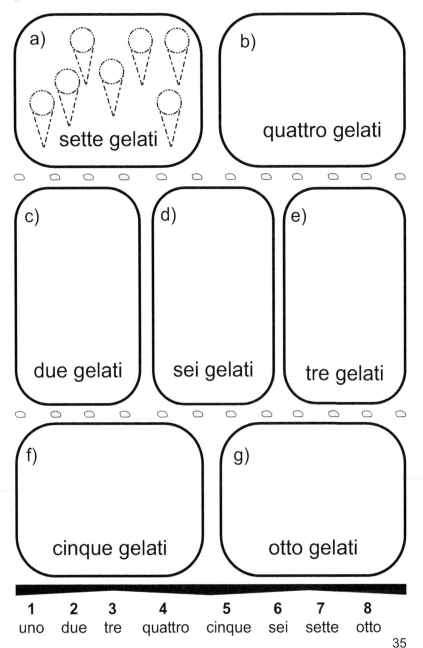

a) sette gelati

b) quattro gelati

c) due gelati

d) sei gelati

e) tre gelati

f) cinque gelati

g) otto gelati

1	2	3	4	5	6	7	8
uno	due	tre	quattro	cinque	sei	sette	otto

35

A holiday resort

Colour the pictures and read the Italian words:

il supermercato

la trattoria

il campeggio

il ristorante

la pizzeria

la gelateria

l'albergo

la spiaggia

il mare

In an Italian town you may see the following signs for some places selling food:

Pizzeria A restaurant selling pizzas

Ristorante A restaurant

Trattoria A restaurant (often family run)

Gelateria An ice cream parlour

In the boxes below, draw something that could be eaten in each of the places:

la gelateria	la pizzeria
il ristorante	la trattoria

l'albergo (the hotel)

_____

i servizi
(the toilets)

l'ascensore
(the lift)

le docce
(the showers)

_____

_____

la piscina
(the swimming pool)

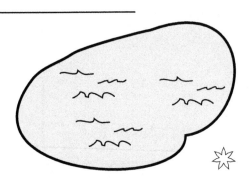

_____

Let's design our own hotel!

Draw a plan of a hotel, and write the Italian words below in the correct places:

il ristorante   i servizi   l'ascensore

la piscina   le docce

Italian quiz

Read the questions, then circle one of the boxes:
(You can look through the book to help you.)

1) How do you say **hi or bye** in Italian?

| ciao | sì | per favore |

2) How do you say **thank you** in Italian?

| Buon giorno | grazie | Arrivederci |

3) What is **strawberry** in Italian?

| limone | cioccolato | fragola |

4) What does **patatine** mean in English?

| chips | chicken | fish |

5) What is **piscina** in English?

| restaurant | swimming pool | showers |

6) What is **un gelato** in English?

| water | a lemonade | an ice cream |

7) What is **la spiaggia** in English?

| the hotel | the beach | the sea |

Answers

Page 3

a) sì   b) ciao   c) per favore   d) Buon giorno

e) grazie   f) Buona notte   g) Arrivederci

Page 4

1) ciao   2) sì   3) grazie   4) arrivederci

5) per favore

Page 5

1a) Bene   b) Così così   c) Male

Page 8

a) due b) sei   c) tre

d) uno e) cinque f) quattro

Page 9

a) Cinque, per favore.
b) Quattro, per favore.
c) Due, per favore.
d) Sei, per favore.
e) Tre, per favore.

Page 10

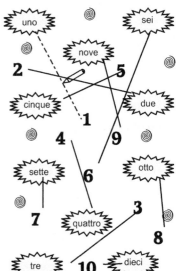

Page 11
sette is missing

Page 13

1) un succo d'arancia   2) un caffè
3) una Coca-Cola   4) un tè
5) una limonata   6) un'acqua minerale

Page 14

1) Vorrei un'acqua minerale, per favore.
2) Vorrei un succo d'arancia, per favore.
3) Vorrei una limonata, per favore.
4) Vorrei una Coca-Cola, per favore.
5) Vorrei un tè, per favore.
6) Vorrei un caffè, per favore.

Page 19

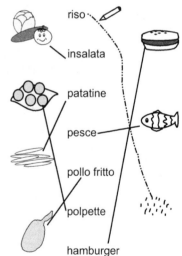

riso
insalata
patatine
pesce
pollo fritto
polpette
hamburger

Page 15
1) No   2) sì   3) No
4) Sì   5) No 6) Sì

Page 17

il cornetto = the croissant
il pane = the bread
i pomodori = the tomatoes
il formaggio = the cheese
la marmellata = the jam
il burro = the butter

Page 20

1) 9 euros 2) 6 euros 3) 8 euros 4) 7 euros
5) 4 euros

Page 21

B	U	R	R	O	E		F
				C			O
			S		P		R
		E		E	A		M
P	P		N		T		A
R		A	I		A		G
O	P		N		T		G
S			S		I		I
C			A		N		O
I			L		E		O
U			A			L	
T			T		L		
T			A	O			
O			P	R	I	S	O
P	O	M	O	D	O	R	I

Page 24

1) Marco   2) Antonio
3) Elena   4) Susanna
5) Anna

Page 25

Spaghetti alla Bolognese
Penne al salmone
Tagliatelle alla carbonara
Ravioli alla napoletana

Page 27

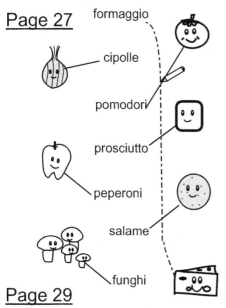

formaggio

cipolle

pomodori

prosciutto

peperoni

salame

funghi

Page 28

The following pizza toppings should be drawn:

1) cheese & tomato
2) ham & mushroom
3) peppers, onions
   & mushrooms
4) salami & onion

Page 29

una pizza con funghi e cipolle
una pizza con salame e prosciutto
una pizza con pomodori, formaggio e pepperoni
una pizza con funghi

Page 31

meat, chicken or fish: salame   pollo fritto   pesce   prosciutto   polpette   hamburger   salmone

vegetables or salad: funghi   insalata   patatine   cipolle   pomodori   peperoni

types of pasta: tagliatelle   spaghetti   farfalle   ravioli   fusilli   penne

Page 33

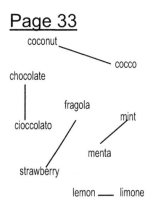

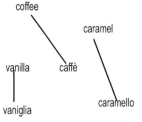

Page 34

Ice creams needing al:
lemon, coconut, coffee
chocolate & caramel

Ice creams needing alla
vanilla strawberry & mint

Page 35

The following number of
Ice creams should be drawn:

a) 7   b) 4   c) 2   d) 6
e) 3   f) 5   g) 8

Page 40

1) ciao   2) grazie   3) fragola   4) chips

5) swimming pool   6) an ice cream   7) the beach

44

Challenges to speak Italian on holiday

The next part of this book contains various challenges to speak Italian whilst in Italy. It's so nice speaking Italian, so it's going to be fun!

The challenges are flexible, so for the challenges containing food, if you don't eat any of the things outlined in the challenges, then you can change the challenge to something else.

On many of the challenge pages there is an alternative challenge, but if you prefer you can think of your own alternative challenge.

Tick the target achieved box when you have completed the challenge. How many of the challenges can you do?

Once you have been to Italy, write in the star how many of the challenges you completed.

Can I say hello in Italian?

For this challenge, you need to say hello in Italian using either:

Ciao .... Hi

Buon giorno .... Good day

(This phrase is only used during the day time)

For an additional challenge, also try and use the following two phrases:

Buona sera..................... Good evening

Buona notte .... Good night

If you use all 4 Italian phrases during your holiday you can tick the challenge achieved box twice.

Challenge achieved

Tick when completed

Can I say goodbye in Italian?

For this challenge, you need to say goodbye in Italian using either of the two phrases:

Ciao! .... Bye

Arrivederci! .... Goodbye

(Ciao can mean either Hi or Bye)

Listen to how Italians say goodbye to you. Is there one phrase they use more than the other?

 —————————————

For an additional challenge, see how many people you can say good bye to in Italian on any one day, and write the number in the star:

Challenge achieved

Tick when completed

Can I say thank you in Italian?

It's nice to be polite and say thank you for things, so for this challenge you have to say thank you in Italian at least five times during your holiday.

To say thank you in Italian we say **grazie**.

Colour in or tick each box each time you say grazie:

grazie

Challenge achieved

Tick when completed

Can I ask for a map in Italian?

Tourist information centres and many hotels have town / city maps. It can be useful to ask for a map, either to help you find where you want to go, or to have as a souvenir.

For this challenge, you have to ask for a map in Italian:

Una mappa, per favore.

una mappa .... a map

per favore .... please

Challenge
achieved

Tick when completed

Can I order some Bruschette?

Bruschetta is grilled Italian bread topped with tomatoes, basil, garlic and olive oil. It is very tasty, and makes a lovely starter. Bruschetta can also be ordered with cheese on top. To ask for it with cheese order **Bruschette con formaggio**. Bruschetta becomes **bruschette** in the plural (more than one). For this challenge you need to order some Bruschette, and remember to say please.

Bruschette, per favore.

Alternative challenge:

If you don't want to order Bruschetta, order something different in Italian. Remember to say **per favore.**

Challenge achieved

Tick when completed

Can I order a drink in Italian?

For this challenge you need to choose and order a drink in Italian:
(Remember to say per favore (please) after the drink)

una Coca-Cola ………. a coke

una Coca-Cola light….. a diet coke

una limonata ………… a lemonade

un'acqua minerale…… a mineral water

un succo d'arancia……an orange juice

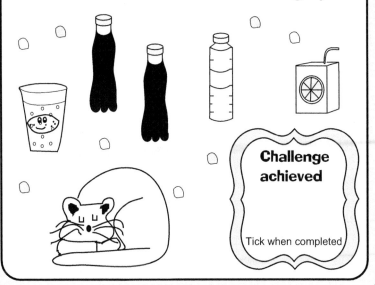

Challenge achieved

Tick when completed

Can I ask where the toilets are?

For this challenge you need to ask in Italian where the toilets are:

Dov'è la toilette?

Useful phrases:

Dov'è la toilette?   Where is the toilet?

Dove sono i servizi?   Where are the toilets?

Dopo il bar   After the bar

A sinistra   On the left

A destra   On the right

servizi   toilets

uomini   men

donne   women

Challenge achieved

Tick when completed

Can I buy some Italian cheese?

Italy is famous for it's production of cheese. For this challenge you need to ask for ONE type of cheese.

Here are some useful phrases

Cinquanta grammi di ......50 grams of

Cento grammi di ....100 grams of

Duecento grammi di ......200 grams of

Here are some typical Italian cheeses:

Grana padano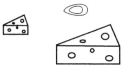

Parmigiano reggiano

Mozzarella

Pecorino romano

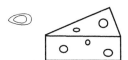

Challenge achieved

Tick when completed

> ## Can I ask if a supermarket sells torrone?

Torrone is an Italian nougat made using **nuts**, honey and sugar. The traditional Italian torrone uses almonds, but there are lots of tasty varities.

For this challenge ask if a supermarket sells torrone, and if they do, find it on the shelf. **If you have a nut allergy ask if the supermarket has strawberries.**

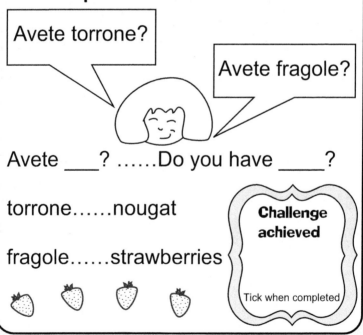

Avete torrone?

Avete fragole?

Avete ___? ......Do you have ____?

torrone......nougat

fragole......strawberries

Challenge achieved

Tick when completed

Can I order some pasta or a pizza in Italian?

Italian pizzas and pasta dishes are so tasty! For this challenge you have to order a pizza or some pasta in Italian. (See pages 22-29)

Una pizza con prosciutto e funghi, per favore.

(The boy above is ordering a ham and mushroom pizza but you can order a different pizza or pasta dish).

If you don't eat pizza or pasta, choose something different.

Challenge achieved

Tick when completed

Can I ask for the bill in Italian?

After a meal or having some drinks, challenge yourself to ask for the bill in Italian:

> Il conto, per favore.

il conto .... the bill

per favore .... please

Pizza	€ 5
Limonata	€ 2
Gelato	€ 3
	€10

Challenge achieved

Tick when completed

What ice cream flavours can I see?

For this challenge, you need to go to a shop which sells ice creams and tick which ice cream flavours are for sale:

- ☐ fragola
- ☐ vaniglia
- ☐ cioccolato
- ☐ cocco
- ☐ menta
- ☐ caramello
- ☐ limone
- ☐ caffè

Challenge achieved

Tick when completed

Can I buy an ice cream in Italian?

Italy is famous for it's lovely ice creams!
For this challenge you need to ask for
an ice cream in Italian:

Useful words

un gelato alla vaniglia - a vanilla ice cream

un gelato alla fragola - a strawberry ice cream

un gelato al cioccolato - a chocolate ice cream

Un gelato alla vaniglia,
per favore.

See pages 32 - 34
for additional
ice cream flavours.

**Challenge
achieved**

Tick when completed

Alternative challenge: order an
orange juice:
Un succo d'arancia, per favore.

What can I see in my holiday resort?

Look out for the following signs around your holiday resort, and tick the box if you see the sign:

☐ **SUPERMERCATO**

☐ **PIZZERIA**

☐ **GELATARIA**

☐ **RISTORANTE**

☐ **TRATTORIA**

☐ **ALBERGO**

☐ **SPIAGGIA**

Note: You can tick the target achieved box even if you don't find all the signs as some signs may not be in your holiday resort.

Challenge achieved

Tick when completed

Can I ask when there is a market?

Italian markets can be great for buying some fresh fruit or some lovely holiday souvenirs. For this challenge you need to ask when there is a market.

> Quando c'è il mercato?

Tick which day or days there is a market in your resort

- [ ] lunedì (Monday)
- [ ] martedì (Tuesday)
- [ ] mercoledì (Wednesday)
- [ ] giovedì (Thursday)
- [ ] venerdì (Friday)
- [ ] sabato (Saturday)
- [ ] domenica (Sunday)

Challenge achieved

Tick when completed

	Italian		English
un'	acqua minerale		mineral water
l'	albergo	the	hotel
all'	arrabbiata		spicy tomato sauce
	arrivederci		good bye
l'	ascensore	the	lift
	Avete…..?		Do you have……?
	bene		good
alla	bolognese		meat pasta sauce
	bruschetta		tomato & garlic bread
	buon giorno		good day
	buon pomeriggio		good afternoon
	buona sera		good evening
il	burro	the	butter
alla	carbonara		bacon & cream sauce
	caffè		coffee
il	campeggio	the	campsite
	caramello		caramel
	ciao		hi or bye
	cinque		five
	cioccolato		chocolate
	cipolle		onions
una	Coca-Cola	a	Coca-Cola
una	Coca-Cola light	a	diet Coca-Cola
	cocco		coconut
	Come stai?		How are you?
	con		with
il	conto	the	bill
il	cornetto	the	croissant
	così così		so so
	dieci		ten
le	docce	the	showers
	domenica		Sunday
	due		two

61

Italian		English	
	farfalle		pasta bows
	formaggio		cheese
	fragola		strawberry
	funghi		mushrooms
	fusilli		pasta spirals
la	gelateria	the	ice cream shop
	gelati		ice creams
un	gelato	an	ice cream
	giovedì		Thursday
	grazie		thank you
	hamburger		hamburger
	insalata		salad
una	limonata	a	lemonade
	limone		lemon
	lunedì		Monday
	male		not so good
una	mappa	a	map
il	mare	the	sea
la	marmellata	the	jam
	martedì		Tuesday
	menta		mint
il	mercato	the	market
	mercoledì		Wednesday
	Mi chiamo…..		My name is…..
alla	napoletana		tomato pasta sauce
	no		no
	nove		nine
	otto		eight
il	pane	the	bread
	panna		cream
	patatine		chips
	penne		tubes of pasta
	peperoni		peppers

Italian		English
	Italian	**English**
	per favore	please
	pesce	fish
	pesto	basil, oil and garlic sauce
la	piscina	the swimming pool
la	pizzeria	the pizza restaurant
	pollo	chicken
	polpette	meatballs
i	pomodori	the tomatoes
il	prosciutto	the ham
	quattro	four
	ravioli	filled pasta shapes
	riso	rice
il	ristorante	the restaurant
	sabato	Saturday
	salame	salami
	salmone	salmon
	sei	six
i	servizi	the toilets
	sette	seven
	sì	yes
	spaghetti	thin strips of pasta
la	spiaggia	the beach
un	succo d'arancia	an orange juice
il	supermercato	the supermarket
	tagliatelle	thick strips of pasta
un	tè	a tea
	torrone	Italian nougat
la	trattoria	the restaurant
	tre	three
	uno	one
	vaniglia	vanilla
	venerdì	Friday
	vorrei	I would like

63

Also available by Joanne Leyland:

French
Young Cool Kids Learn French
Cool Kids Speak French (books 1, 2 & 3)
French Word Games - Cool Kids Speak French
40 Word Searches In French Cool Kids Speak French
First 100 Words In French Coloring Book Cool Kids Speak French
Cool Kids Speak French - Special Christmas Edition
On Holiday In France Cool Kids Speak French
Cool Kids Do Maths In French
Un Alien Sur La Terre
Le Singe Qui Change De Couleur
Tu As Un Animal?

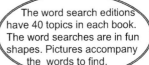
The first 100 words colouring book editions have 3 or 4 words per page, and are ideal for those who like to colour as they learn.

Italian
Young Cool Kids Learn Italian
Cool Kids Speak Italian (books 1, 2 & 3)
Italian Word Games - Cool Kids Speak Italian
40 Word Searches In Italian Cool Kids Speak Italian
First 100 Words In Italian Coloring Book Cool Kids Speak Italian
On Holiday In Italy Cool Kids Speak Italian
Un Alieno Sulla Terra
La Scimmia Che Cambia Colore
Hai Un Animale Domestico?

The word search editions have 40 topics in each book. The word searches are in fun shapes. Pictures accompany the words to find.

German
Young Cool Kids Learn German
Cool Kids Speak German (books 1, 2 & 3)
German Word Games - Cool Kids Speak German
40 Word Searches In German Cool Kids Speak German
First 100 Words In German Coloring Book Cool Kids Speak German

Spanish
Young Cool Kids Learn Spanish
Cool Kids Speak Spanish (books 1, 2 & 3)
Spanish Word Games - Cool Kids Speak Spanish
40 Word Searches In Spanish Cool Kids Speak Spanish
First 100 Words In Spanish Coloring Book Cool Kids Speak Spanish
Cool Kids Speak Spanish - Special Christmas Edition
On Holiday In Spain Cool Kids Speak Spanish
Cool Kids Do Maths In Spanish
Un Extraterrestre En La Tierra
El Mono Que Cambia De Color
Seis Mascotas Maravillosas

If you like games, you could try the word game editions.